TRY NOT TO LAUGH CHALLENGE™

WOULD YOU RATHER?

• • • • • • • • • • • • • • • • • • • •

EWW!
EDITION

Try Not To Laugh Challenge
BONUS PLAY

Join our Joke Club and get the Bonus Play PDF!

Simply send us an email to:

TNTLPublishing@gmail.com

and you will get the following:

- 10 Hilarious Would You Rather Questions
- An entry in our Monthly Giveaway of a $50 Amazon Gift card!

We draw a new winner each month and will contact you via email!

Good luck!

Welcome to
The Try Not to Laugh Challenge
Would You Rather?
EWW EDITION

RULES:

• Face your opponent and decide who is
'Player 1' and 'Player 2'.

• Starting with 'Player 1', read the Would You Rather
question aloud and pick an answer. The same player
will then explain why they chose that answer in the
most hilarious or wacky way possible!

• If the reason makes 'Player 2' laugh, then a laugh
point is scored!

• Take turns going back and forth, then mark your
total laugh points at the end of each round!

• Whoever gets the most laugh points is officially
crowned the 'Laugh Master'!

• If ending with a tie, finish with the Tie-Breaker
round for WINNER TAKES ALL!

Most importantly, have fun and be SILLY! 😊

CRAZY COREY

REMEMBER, these scenarios listed in the
book are solely for fun and games!
Please do NOT attempt any of the crazy
scenarios in this book.

7

ROUND

1

Player 1:

(DON'T FORGET TO EXPLAIN YOUR ANSWERS!)

Would you rather have a foot for a face OR have worms come out of your nose, every time you sneeze?

Laugh Point____ /1

Would you rather lick the dirty cafeteria floor OR stick your face in the toilet for 1 minute?

Laugh Point____ /1

10

Player 1:

(DON'T FORGET TO EXPLAIN YOUR ANSWERS!)

Would you rather eat a pine cone covered in peanut butter, OR eat a hay and grass salad with mud dressing?

Laugh Point _____ /1

Would you rather have footlong fingernails OR footlong toenails?

Laugh Point _____ /1

Pass the book to Player 2! →

Player 2:

(DON'T FORGET TO EXPLAIN YOUR ANSWERS!)

Would you rather wear footie pajamas everywhere you go, OR constantly wear a diaper as pants?

Laugh Point___ /1

Would you rather explode like a shaken Coca-Cola can when you get angry, OR pop open like a can of biscuits when you bottle up your emotions?

Laugh Point___9/1

Player 2

Would you rather wrestle a giant, sweaty sumo wrestling elephant, OR play contact football with a shedding, spastic panda?

Laugh Point_____/1

Would you rather sleep on the dirty concrete for a month OR sleep in a pigsty for a week?

Laugh Point_____/1

13

Player **1** : <u>0</u> **/4**
ROUND TOTAL

Player **2** : <u>0.9</u>**/4**
ROUND TOTAL

<u>BoB</u>

ROUND
CHAMPION

ROUND 2

Player 1

Would you rather build a gingerbread house out of living roly poly's and cement, OR make a giant Christmas cake out of ear wax and trash remains?

Laugh Point____ /1

Would you rather wear a fish-scented jacket on a first date, OR an onion-scented hat when meeting your favorite celebrity?

Laugh Point____ /1

Player 1

(DON'T FORGET TO EXPLAIN YOUR ANSWERS!)

Would you rather eat a rotten squid donut with eyeball sprinkles, OR snack on dried scabs with a side of rotten toenails?

Laugh Point_____ /1

Would you rather clean a litter box with your bare hands OR clean a cat using only your tongue?

Laugh Point_____ /1

Pass the book to Player 2! →

17

Player 2

(DON'T FORGET TO EXPLAIN YOUR ANSWERS!)

Would you rather have to drink a cup of spoiled milk OR wash your face with rotten sour cream?

Laugh Point_____/1

Would you rather have toenails that were six inches long OR nose hairs that looked like a mustache?

Laugh Point_____/1

Player 2

(DON'T FORGET TO EXPLAIN YOUR ANSWERS!)

Would you rather touch your grandpa's sweaty armpit OR rub your grandma's feet after a long day in the sun?

Laugh Point____ /1

Would you rather wear melted caramel as sunscreen OR sticky, hot fudge as lotion?

Laugh Point____ /1

19

Player **1** : _____ **/4**
ROUND TOTAL

Player **2** : _____ **/4**
ROUND TOTAL

_____
ROUND
CHAMPION

ROUND 3

Player 1

Would you rather only be able to smell sweaty armpits OR dirty diapers for the rest of your life?

Laugh Point____/1

Would you rather have to mow the yard by eating the grass OR clean the gutters by drinking the water?

Laugh Point____/1

Player 1

Would you rather walk on a carpet made of cockroaches OR swim in a bathtub filled with living worms?

Laugh Point____/1

Would you rather have to smell rotten food all day OR smell the spray of a skunk all night?

Laugh Point____/1

Pass the book to Player 2! →

Player 2:

Would you rather smell like freshly cut fish OR rotten eggs?

Laugh Point____ /1

Would you rather be a scientist, who accidentally creates an alien virus that infects everybody in the world, OR be the inventor of the newest brand of hairspray, that poisons every animal in the world?

Laugh Point____ /1

Player 2

Would you rather wear a necklace made of old teeth OR a bracelet made out of beetles?

Laugh Point____ /1

Would you rather hold your breath until you turn purple OR help your great grandmother pluck her upper lip hairs?

Laugh Point____ /1

Player **1** : ____ **/4**
ROUND TOTAL

Player **2** : ____ **/4**
ROUND TOTAL

____
ROUND
CHAMPION

ROUND

4

Player 1

Would you rather live in a world where toilet paper can talk, and constantly comments on how bad you smell OR have to use a deodorant that bites every time you use it?

Laugh Point____ /1

Would you rather eat a chicken liver pie OR a cow liver cake?

Laugh Point____ /1

28

Player 1:

(DON'T FORGET TO EXPLAIN YOUR ANSWERS!)

Would you rather slide down a sizzling hot, metal slide in the middle of summer, OR crawl on your hands and knees across a across a splintered, wooden drawbridge in the middle of winter?

Laugh Point_____ /1

Would you rather live in a spider-infested treehouse, OR in a cave occupied by 100 bats?

Laugh Point_____ /1

Pass the book to Player 2! →

Player 2:

Would you rather have eight eyes, like a spider OR six limbs, like a cockroach?

Laugh Point____ /1

Would you rather build a large Ferris wheel out of the hottest peppers in the world with your bare hands, OR make a two-story cabin out of maple syrup and moldy bologna with your bare hands?

Laugh Point____ /1

Player 2

Would you rather drink someone else's snot OR eat someone else's earwax?

Laugh Point____/1

Would you rather your stomach have a window, so you can see your food being digested, OR your hands have no skin, so you can see the muscles work when you move them?

Laugh Point____/1

Player **1** : ___ /4
ROUND TOTAL

Player **2** : ___ /4
ROUND TOTAL

___
ROUND
CHAMPION

ROUND

5

Player 1

Would you rather have mushroom pizza as your skin OR zucchini noodles as your hair?

Laugh Point_____ /1

Would you rather use your schools Lost and Found box to dress yourself every morning, OR eat whatever is left in old lunch boxes as lunch?

Laugh Point_____ /1

Player 1

(DON'T FORGET TO EXPLAIN YOUR ANSWERS!)

Would you rather eat an entire loaf of fruitcake, without anything to wash it down OR drink a milkshake made with black olives?

Laugh Point_____ /1

Would you rather eat a giant, hot pepper-flavored sundae OR a huge raw egg and spinach milkshake?

Laugh Point_____ /1

Pass the book to Player 2! →

Player 2:

Would you rather have a hat made of sticky, itchy cotton candy stuck on your head, OR shoes made of slippery, gooey slime stuck on your feet?

Laugh Point____ /1

Would you rather find $1,000 while on an adventure in the woods, but get swarmed by wasps OR find $1,000 in a chest at the bottom of the lake, but get attacked by leeches?

Laugh Point____ /1

36

Player 2

(DON'T FORGET TO EXPLAIN YOUR ANSWERS!)

Would you rather finger paint with sticky, melted Jolly Ranchers OR sculpt a statue with stale, buttery popcorn?

Laugh Point____/1

Would you rather wear the same socks every day, OR the same used underwear?

Laugh Point____/1

Player **1**: _____ /4
ROUND TOTAL

Player **2**: _____ /4
ROUND TOTAL

_____
ROUND CHAMPION

ROUND

6

Player 1

Would you rather drink a raw egg OR eat a raw onion?

Laugh Point_____ /1

Would you rather sprout a small tree in the middle of your forehead, OR grow an extra hand in your mouth?

Laugh Point_____ /1

Player 1

(DON'T FORGET TO EXPLAIN YOUR ANSWERS!)

Would you rather wear your used socks on your hands for one day OR tie your shoes to your head?

Laugh Point_____/1

Would you rather your mom spit on her finger to wipe a smudge off your cheek in public, OR your dad slicks your hair down with his armpit sweat at home?

Laugh Point_____/1

Pass the book to Player 2! →

Player 2

Would you rather have a lifetime supply of used dental floss OR a lifetime supply of dirty socks?

Laugh Point____ /1

Would you rather recreate the Eiffel Tower out of dry spaghetti noodles, OR repaint the Mona Lisa using a toothbrush?

Laugh Point____ /1

42

Player 2:

Would you rather crawl through a 15-foot sewer, OR get pooped on by a dinosaur?

Laugh Point____ /1

Would you rather have all your teeth fall out OR all your eyebrow hairs fall off?

Laugh Point____ /1

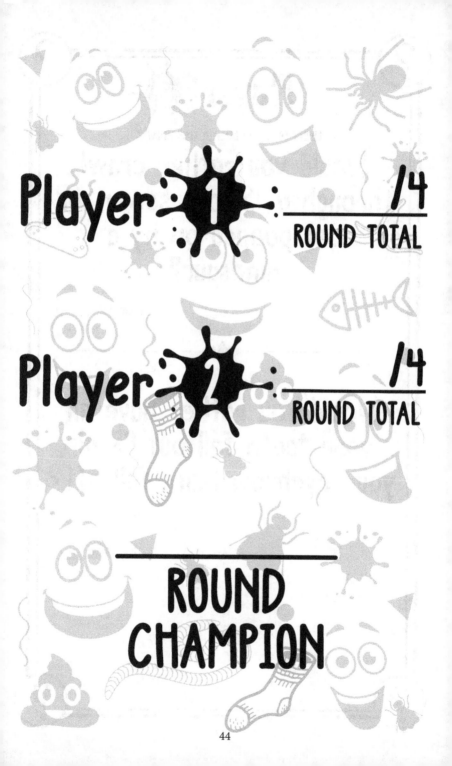

Player **1** : _____ /4
ROUND TOTAL

Player **2** : _____ /4
ROUND TOTAL

_____
ROUND CHAMPION

44

ROUND

7

Player 1

Would you rather always feel like you have to sneeze OR always have a booger hanging out of your nose?

Laugh Point____ /1

Would you rather live the life of an earthworm OR live the life of a flying cockroach?

Laugh Point____ /1

Player 1

Would you rather hand-feed green peas to a snake OR feed squishy, rotten hamburger meat to a vulture?

Laugh Point_____ /1

Would you rather eat the dirty bark from your school's playground, OR drink the dirty sidewalk water with a straw?

Laugh Point_____ /1

Pass the book to Player 2! →

Player 2

(DON'T FORGET TO EXPLAIN YOUR ANSWERS!)

Would you rather fall headfirst into a vat of Rocky Road ice cream, OR dive into a massive bowl of Flamin' Hot Cheetos?

Laugh Point____/1

Would you rather stink like a fresh eye-watering onion OR only be able to taste onions, and nothing else for a whole year?

Laugh Point____/1

48

Player 2

Would you rather have to clean all the toilets in your town, OR have to smooch all the dirtiest people in your city?

Laugh Point____ /1

Would you rather have one of your fingers shaped like a fork, OR one of your toes shaped like a spoon?

Laugh Point____ /1

Player  1 : _____ /4
ROUND TOTAL

Player 2 : _____ /4
ROUND TOTAL

_____
ROUND
CHAMPION

ROUND

8

Player 1

Would you rather accidentally mistake a science experiment for something to drink, and turn into a toxic, purple gumdrop OR accidentally swallow a piece of chocolate from the lunchroom, that turns you into a brown, moldy pumpkin?

Laugh Point_____/1

Would you rather eat a raw fish OR a raw chicken?

Laugh Point_____/1

Player 1

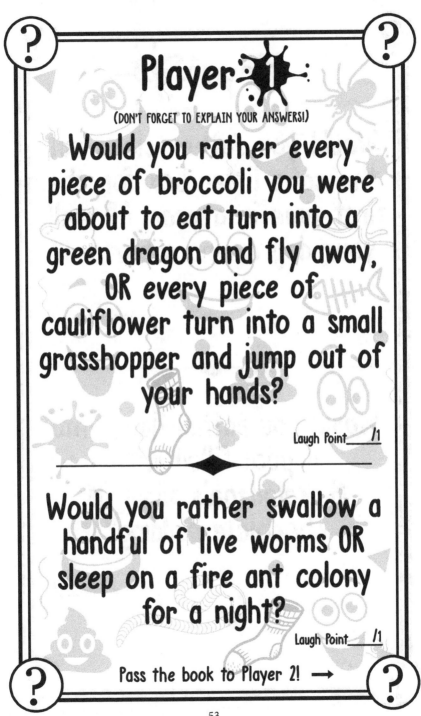

(DON'T FORGET TO EXPLAIN YOUR ANSWERS!)

Would you rather every piece of broccoli you were about to eat turn into a green dragon and fly away, OR every piece of cauliflower turn into a small grasshopper and jump out of your hands?

Laugh Point_____ /1

Would you rather swallow a handful of live worms OR sleep on a fire ant colony for a night?

Laugh Point_____ /1

Pass the book to Player 2! →

Player 2

Would you rather clean out the cat's litter box for the first time in a year, OR walk your dog during a blizzard?

Laugh Point_____ /1

Would you rather jump into a pool filled with Nickelodeon's slime OR chocolate pudding?

Laugh Point_____ /1

Player 2

Would you rather be bald OR have dog fur cover your entire body?

Laugh Point____/1

Would you rather have hair down to your knees OR fingernails that are 3-feet long?

Laugh Point____/1

Player  1 : _____ /4

ROUND TOTAL

Player 2 : _____ /4

ROUND TOTAL

_____

ROUND CHAMPION

56

ROUND
9

Player 1

(DON'T FORGET TO EXPLAIN YOUR ANSWERS!)

Would you rather brush your teeth with someone else's toothbrush OR floss with used floss?

Laugh Point____/1

Would you rather smell your gym coach's stinky sock OR smell a stranger's stinky armpit?

Laugh Point____/1

Player 1

Would you rather drink bug juice OR eat a cat's throw up?

Laugh Point_____ /1

Would you rather clip an old lady's toenails OR trim an old man's nose hairs?

Laugh Point_____ /1

Pass the book to Player 2! →

Player 2

Would you rather take a bath in chunky, rotten milk OR take a shower in hot prune juice?

Laugh Point____ /1

Would you rather have snot-filled jelly donuts OR chocolate brownies made out of dog poop?

Laugh Point____ /1

Player 2

Would you rather win an award for 'World's Loudest Burp' OR 'World's Longest Booger'?

Laugh Point____ /1

Would you rather drink a shake made from hot dogs OR drink milk from a dog?

Laugh Point____ /1

Player 1: _____ /4
ROUND TOTAL

Player 2: _____ /4
ROUND TOTAL

_____
ROUND
CHAMPION

ROUND

10

Player 1

Would you rather have small chickens in your mouth that act as teeth and chew your food for you, OR have small flies in your eyes that let you see 10x better?

Laugh Point____ /1

Would you rather burp balls of flame like a dragon, OR be able to spit acid and burn through objects?

Laugh Point____ /1

Player 1

Would you rather every human have fish heads for hands, OR everyone have lobster claws for feet?

Laugh Point_____ /1

Would you rather play football with a beehive as the ball, OR baseball with a sea urchin as the ball and a baguette as the bat?

Laugh Point_____ /1

Pass the book to Player 2! →

Player 2

Would you rather drink the water from a goldfish bowl OR a stranger's used bath?

Laugh Point_____ /1

Would you rather eat a piece of tuna-flavored birthday cake OR cherry-flavored anchovies?

Laugh Point_____ /1

Player 2

Would you rather have skin that smells like cheese OR have to eat cheese that smells like feet?

Laugh Point____ /1

Would you rather eat one large tarantula OR 100 tiny spiders?

Laugh Point____ /1

Player **1**: _____ /4
ROUND TOTAL

Player **2**: _____ /4
ROUND TOTAL

_____
ROUND
CHAMPION

Add up all your points from each round.
The PLAYER with the most points is crowned
The Laugh Master!

In the event of a tie, continue to the Round 11
for the tie-breaker round!

Player  1 : _____
GRAND TOTAL

Player 2 : _____
GRAND TOTAL

_____

The
Laugh Master

Player 1

Would you rather eat a jelly bean that tastes like canned dog food, OR a jelly bean that tastes like stinky socks?

Laugh Point____ /1

Would you rather eat a grilled booger and cheese sandwich OR a grilled worm and cheese panini?

Laugh Point____ /1

Player 1

Would you rather be the target of a pie-throwing contest, OR the star of a dunking booth, filled with jalapeño flavored Jell-O?

Laugh Point_____ /1

Would you rather have flowers and vines as hair OR rubber bands as eyelashes?

Laugh Point_____ /1

Pass the book to Player 2! →

Player 2:

(DON'T FORGET TO EXPLAIN YOUR ANSWERS!)

Would you rather grow hair on your tongue OR fingernails out of your head?

Laugh Point____ /1

Would you rather drink a sardine, sour cream, and salsa smoothie OR eat a chocolate, crab, and curry cupcake?

Laugh Point____ /1

Player 2

(DON'T FORGET TO EXPLAIN YOUR ANSWERS!)

Would you rather eat a bowl of dog food with a fork OR eat a plate of cold spaghetti on the floor, without using your hands?

Laugh Point____ /1

Would you rather have 5 belching brothers OR 5 singing sisters?

Laugh Point____ /1

75

Add up all your points from Round 11.
The PLAYER with the most points is crowned
The Laugh Master!

Player **1**: _____ /4
ROUND TOTAL

Player **2**: _____ /4
ROUND TOTAL

_____
The
Laugh Master